LILLY'S
DAY COPING
WITH AUTISM

BETHANY STOOTS

ILLUSTRATED BY: SYDNEY TRUESDAIL

WRITERS REPUBLIC L.L.C.
515 Summit Ave. Unit R1
Union City, NJ 07087, USA

Website: *www.writersrepublic.com*
Hotline: *1-877-656-6838*
Email: *info@writersrepublic.com*

Ordering Information:
Quantity sales. Special discounts are available on quantity purchases by corporations, associations, and others. For details, contact the publisher at the address above.

Library of Congress Control Number: 2021908428
ISBN-13:   978-1-63728-080-5   [Paperback Edition]
             978-1-63728-062-1   [Digital Edition]

Rev. date: 04/20/2021

Hello, this is Lilly; she looks just like you and me. However, there is a slight difference; she has autism. Autism is a spectrum disorder, meaning it varies from person to person. Lilly has sensory overload disorder. She cannot be around loud noises, flashing lights, crowds, or stressful situations. This causes her daily life to look slightly different than most. Let's see how a day in Lilly's life looks.

At the beginning of her day, Lilly's mom wakes her up and tells her she needs to get dressed for school. This would not be a problem for most people. However, Lilly has touch sensitivity, which causes most things that touch her pain. For instance, her clothes, people hugging her, and high-fiving her causes discomfort.

Discussion question: How would this affect your life?

Once Lilly gets dressed, she and her mom go to the bus stop. She rides a different bus from most students. Her bus is a special-needs bus. She prefers this because it is much quieter than the other ones.

When Lilly gets to school, her class heads straight to recess. Lilly looks around for someone to play with, but nobody wants to play with her. They think she is weird. Lilly is used to this and goes to play by herself.

Discussion question: How would you feel if you were Lilly?

On this day, the class has a school assembly. All the students went except Lilly. School assemblies are too loud and stress her out. Instead, she goes to the special-needs room.

When the class returns, they are very loud. This causes Lilly to stress out and begin stemming. Stemming is a self-stimulatory behavior. In other words, self-soothing. Lilly's stemming is rocking. This motion helps her relax. Stemming is not only done in this way; it can also be done by flapping her hands, spinning, or repeating words.

Discussion question: How do you deal with stress.

While the teacher is quieting everyone down. Elizabeth, one of Lilly's classmates, goes over to Lilly and starts bullying her. She begins calling her hurtful words, making Lilly feel awful. Kaitlyn overhears what is going on. She goes to Elizabeth and tells her what she was doing is wrong and she needs to stop. Elizabeth tells Kaitlyn to go away and mind her own business.

Discussion question: What would you do if you were Kaitlyn?

Kaitlyn tells the teacher, and she goes over and tells Elizabeth to stop. She makes Elizabeth apologize to Lilly. The teacher then has all the students sit down on the carpet. She reads them a story about bullying. The story teaches them bullying is when you hurt or scare someone on purpose; this could be using your words or by an action such as pushing someone or pulling someone's hair. The teacher then explains what autism is and that it can be hard to be around loud noises sometimes, and that is why Lilly is overwhelmed.

When Lilly arrives home, she went straight to her room crying. Her mom walked in and Lilly explains what has happened that day at school. Her mom explains that even after people apologize what they say may still hurt. Just feel it and forgive them and you will feel better.

The next day, Lilly went back to school. She forgave Elizabeth, but would never forget what was said. At recess, Lilly goes to play by herself. However, when Kaitlyn sees this she goes over and begins playing with Lilly. From that day on, Kaitlyn played with Lilly every day at recess. Some people might differ from you. They might act, talk, or even look different, but they should not be treated differently; they are still just like you and me.